Ransom Neutron Stars
Fly, May FLY!
by Kathryn White
Illustrated by Karen Donnelly

Published by Ransom Publishing Ltd.
Unit 7, Brocklands Farm, West Meon, Hampshire GU32 1JN, UK
www.ransom.co.uk

ISBN 978 178591 447 8
First published in 2017

A CIP catalogue record of this book is available from the British Library.

Fly, May FLY!

Kathryn White
Illustrated by Karen Donnelly

In 1942, Britain was at war.

Everybody helped the war effort.

May helped too.

She was an ATA pilot.
She flew planes around the country.
She delivered them to airfields
and factories.

Tonight she must collect a plane.
She must fly it to an airfield in Kent,
in the south of England.

"The fog is bad tonight, May," said her mum. "Please don't go."

"I have to fly, Mum," said May. "It's my job, and the Air Force need the planes."

May gave her mum and her young son a hug. May touched her son's cheek. "I'll come back soon," she said to him. Then she walked to the car waiting outside.

They drove to the hanger.

When May saw the plane, she smiled with pride.

The plane had been shot down. Its wings had been torn, its body ripped. One engine did not work.

Now, after its repair, the plane was like new. It looked amazing.

"Take care, it's a bad night," warned her officer.

"I will," said May. "But we need this machine in the air, fighting the enemy," said May, bravely.

May pulled on her gloves and climbed
into the cockpit.
She knew this plane. It was a night
fighter.
She had flown these planes before.

She fired up the twin engines and the plane choked into life. The engines sounded strong.

May taxied the plane onto the runway. Soon she was speeding along, then rising up into the darkness of the night.

Seven hours later, May stood on the runway of another airfield.

The sun was rising above the horizon.

May watched the pilot dip the wings of her plane. Then he flew over her head and into battle.

May waved at the plane.

It had been a long night, but she had delivered the plane.

She had helped keep the Air Force flying for another day. Her family, and many other families, would stay safe.

Have you read?

Awesome ATAs

by Kathryn White

Wolves

by Jill Atkins

Have you read?

The Care Home

by Alice Hemming

How to Start Your Own Crazy Cult

by Stephen Rickard

Ransom Neutron Stars

Fly, May FLY!
Word count **320**

Green Book Band

Phonics

Phonics 1	Not Pop, Not Rock Go to the Laptop Man Gus and the Tin of Ham	*Phonics 2*	Deep in the Dark Woods Night Combat Ben's Jerk Chicken Van
Phonics 3	GBH Steel Pan Traffic Jam Platform 7	*Phonics 4*	The Rock Show Gaps in the Brain New Kinds of Energy

Book bands

Pink	Curry! Free Runners My Toys	*Red*	Shopping with Zombies Into the Scanner Planting My Garden
Yellow	Fit for Love The Lottery Ticket In the Stars	*Blue*	Awesome ATAs Wolves The Giant Jigsaw
Green	**Fly, May FLY!** How to Start Your Own Crazy Cult The Care Home	*Orange*	Text Me The Last Soldier Best Friends